Play this game on the beach or in the park. All you need is an empty lunchbox!

TREASURE HUNT

Each player needs an empty box of their own. You have ten minutes to collect as many things from the list as possible. The winner is the person with the most items.

NEVER WANDER OUT OF SIGHT OF THE GROWN UP(S) YOU ARE WITH. MAKE SURE YOU DON'T COLLECT ANYTHING SHARP, AND WASH YOUR HANDS WHEN YOU HAVE FINISHED.

Things to collect:

Smooth stone

Piece of wood

Something made of plastic

Y-shaped twig

Something green

Something with a pattern on it

Something with writing on it

A thing beginning with B

An item with a hole in

A pebble smaller than a penny

Fill in the 5 times table to get to the top of the towers.

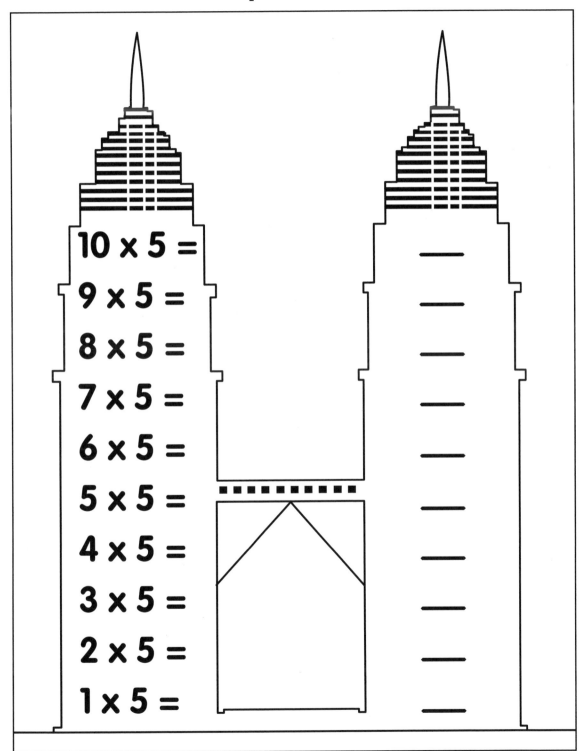

10 x 5 =

9 x 5 =

8 x 5 =

7 x 5 =

6 x 5 =

5 x 5 =

4 x 5 =

3 x 5 =

2 x 5 =

1 x 5 =

Solve the sudoku puzzles so that every row, column and mini-grid has the six symbols.

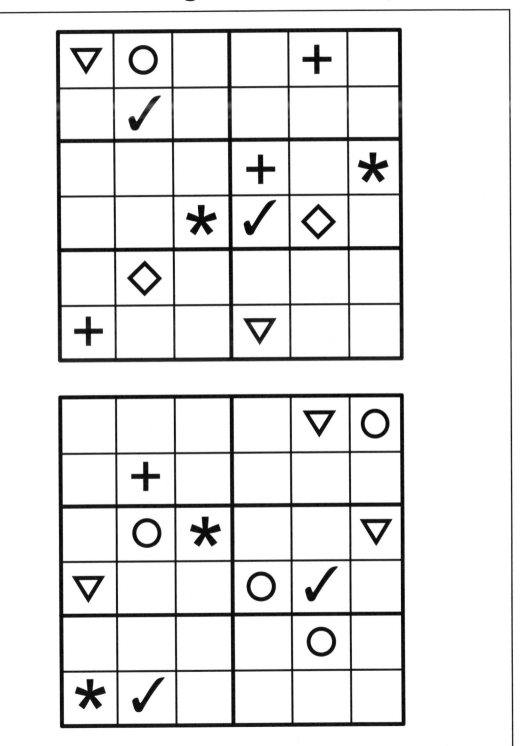

Which silhouette belongs to Ben?

Match the capital cities to the country each is in, then find the cities in the grid.

```
L P C O P E N H A G E N
C I A A R R E B N A C A
D S M S S U P E M O R O
N I A A G C A R A C A S
O R D A I F O S C R T C
T A R A B U D A P E S T
G P I N O N A W A T T O
N O D N O L B E R N B K
I T T E M O S C O W E Y
H I R I O L D C A I R O
S U E V B R U S S E L S
A Q B E I J I N G S I S
W E L L I N G T O N N K
```

CITIES

Accra	Lima	Sofia
Beijing	London	Tokyo
Berlin	Madrid	Vienna
Bern	Moscow	Washington DC
Brussels	Oslo	Wellington
Budapest	Ottawa	
Cairo	Paris	
Canberra	Prague	
Caracas	Quito	
Copenhagen	Rome	

COUNTRIES

Australia	Egypt	Peru
Austria	France	Russia
Belgium	Germany	Spain
Bulgaria	Ghana	Switzerland
Canada	Hungary	United Kingdom
China	Italy	USA
Czech Republic	Japan	Venezuela
Denmark	New Zealand	
Ecuador	Norway	

Use the letters that are left in the grid to spell out something you have to pass in the airport.

You need 2 or more players for this outdoor game.

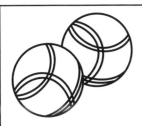 

COOL BOULES!

Boules is a popular game in France, but it's great fun to play wherever you are. The name simply means "balls". If you don't have a boules set, look for stones to play with. You need 2 larger stones for each player, and a small stone to share.

The first player has to throw the small stone (the "jack") about 5 metres away. She then has to throw one of her own stones as close to the jack as possible.

Take turns to throw your first stone, as close to the jack as you can. Make sure you choose stones that are different from each other to tell them apart, or write your initials on them.

Each player then throws their second stone. The winner is the person whose stone is closest to the jack, so throw carefully. If you can't throw it close, try to knock the jack or any other stones out of the way.

Use the compass at the bottom of the map to help answer the questions.

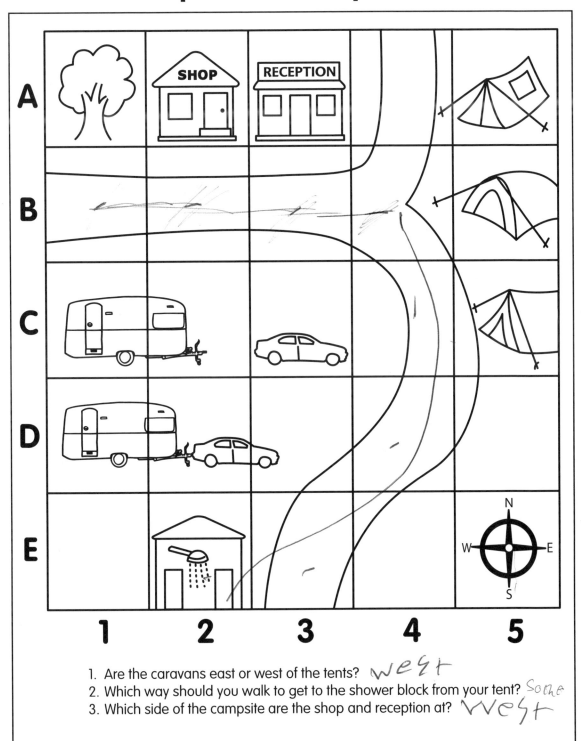

1. Are the caravans east or west of the tents? west
2. Which way should you walk to get to the shower block from your tent? Some
3. Which side of the campsite are the shop and reception at? west

Can you count how many flags there are jumbled in this picture? 9

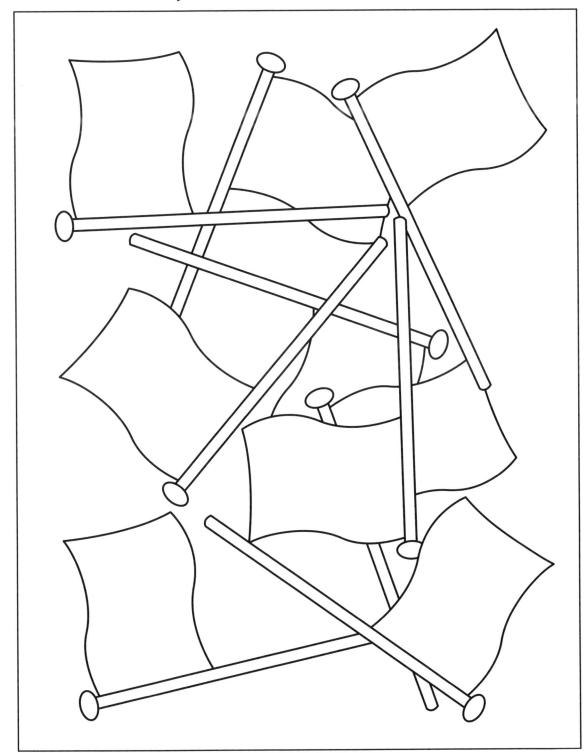

Solve the sudoku puzzles so that every row, column and mini-grid has the letters A to F.

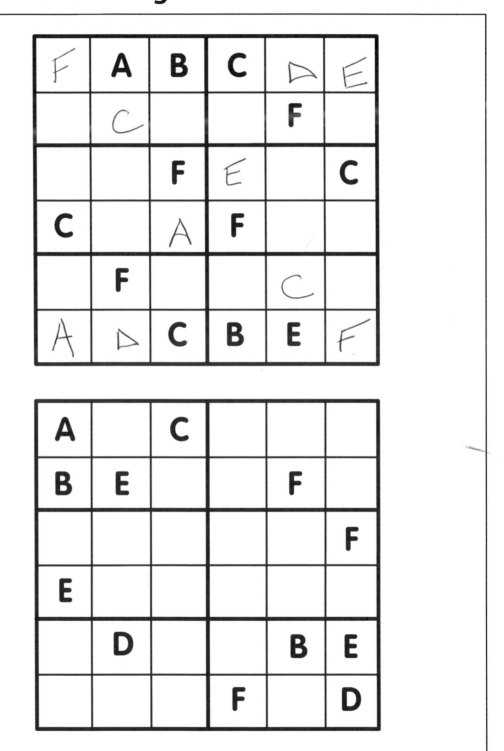

You can play this game anywhere, as long as you can see things outside.

 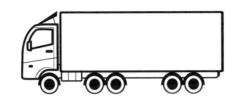 

TWO BY TWO

Choose an item you can see out of the window. The other players have to spot a matching one as you travel along (like playing "Snap" with real objects). They choose an item for you to look for at the same time.

Score a point when somebody sees a chosen item, and then choose a new object for each player to stop you getting bored.

Things to spot:

Red tree

Hedge with berries

Limousine

Supermarket truck

Triangular sign

Hovering bird

Purple car

House in a field

Bike

Fill in the blanks to complete the crossword.

ACROSS

1. Stars and _____
4. _____ that door!
5. _____ and rain
7. _____ is short for miles per hour
8. _____, sea and sand
9. Mermaids live _____ the sea
11. _____ goes the weasel
12. The _____ and the Pussycat
13. You've got a _____ loose!
15. Just a _____, I'm coming!
17. He's good at _____ reading in the car
19. She snowboards but he _____ in the snow
20. _____ down, you move too fast
21. _____ show

DOWN

1. North and _____
2. Madagascar is an _____
3. Windmills and yachts both have _____
4. Nickname for the USA, Uncle _____
6. Bears, foxes, lions and wolves all live in a _____
9. Life has its _____ and downs
10. _____, _____, _____ your boat
14. Burger _____ is a bit like ketchup
15. To get help you must signal _____
16. A steep rock face at the coast is a _____
17. Water_____ is red inside with black pips
18. Don't pick a prickly pear by the _____, try to use the claw!

27

What's that flying through the sky?

This is a great outdoor game if you have lots of people to join in.

MONSTER MASH

Draw lines in the sand, or use chalk on the ground to mark out the two banks of a river. You can spread out skipping ropes instead, if you have them.

Two players link arms to make the monster. They have to stay inside the river banks and try to catch the other players as they try to cross the river. Anyone who is caught links arms too, so the monster grows bigger and more difficult to escape from! The winner is the last player to avoid being caught.

Can you spot 6 differences between these pictures?

Match each flag to its country, and then find the countries hidden in the grid.

```
S  A  I  I  I  A  M  W  A  L  B  J
B  W  G  S  S  O  T  B  K  S  A
R  S  I  R  R  B  R  S  K  A  P
S  O  U  T  H  A  F  R  I  C  A
P  A  E  A  Z  E  E  A  N  C  N
C  C  S  I  F  E  G  L  D  S  M
H  H  L  A  M  O  R  O  C  C  O
I  I  S  O  U  F  R  L  G  A  R
L  N  N  A  T  S  I  K  A  P  J
S  A  N  E  C  E  E  R  G  N  A
W  A  L  E  S  I  B  R  A  Z  D
```

BRAZIL
CHINA
GREECE
ISRAEL
JAPAN
MOROCCO
PAKISTAN
SOUTH AFRICA
SWITZERLAND
WALES

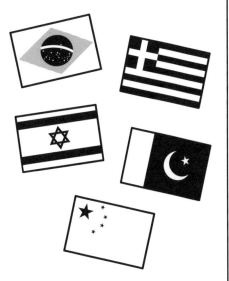

Find the quickest way past the rocks and sharks to reach the lighthouse.

There are four famous sights scrambled here. Use the picture clues to help work them out.

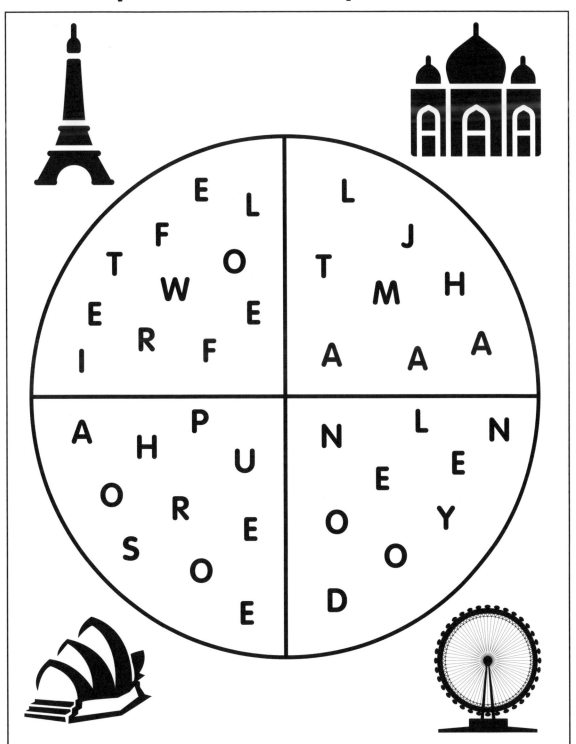

THIS OLD MAN

You might know this rhyme already,
but it doesn't matter if you don't.
Simply say the words out loud,
or sing them if you know the tune:

This old man, he played one,

He played "nick nack" on my _____ .

With a nick, nack, paddy wack,

Give a dog a bone,

This old man came rolling home.

When you get to the blank space, fill in a word that rhymes with "one".

It can be serious or downright silly, it's up to you!

Sing the song again and again, counting up each time.

Solve the sudoku puzzles so that every row, column and mini-grid has the numbers 1-6.

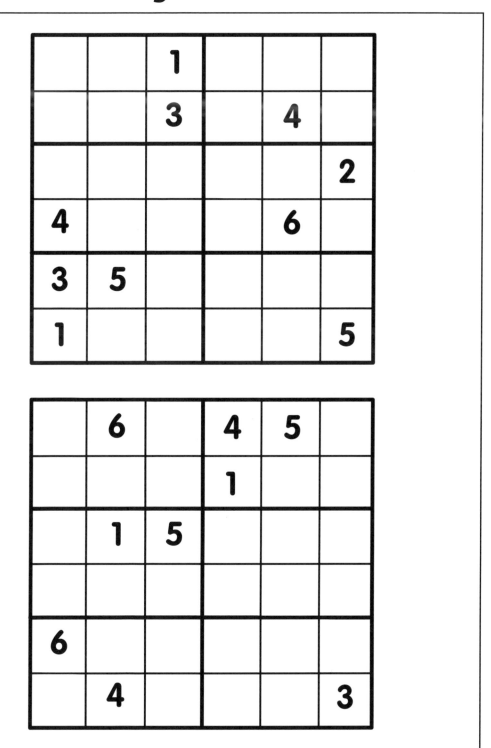

Colour in the peacock to make it even more spectacular.

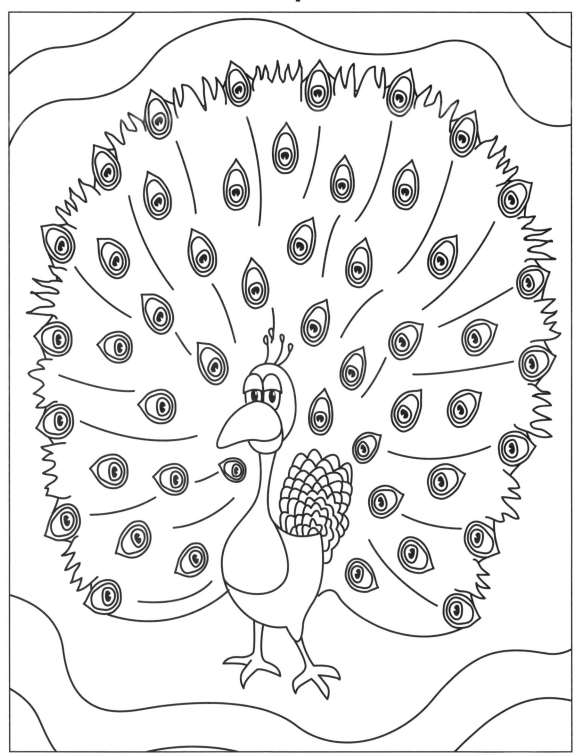

Set sail to see which of the islands is suitable for your holiday.

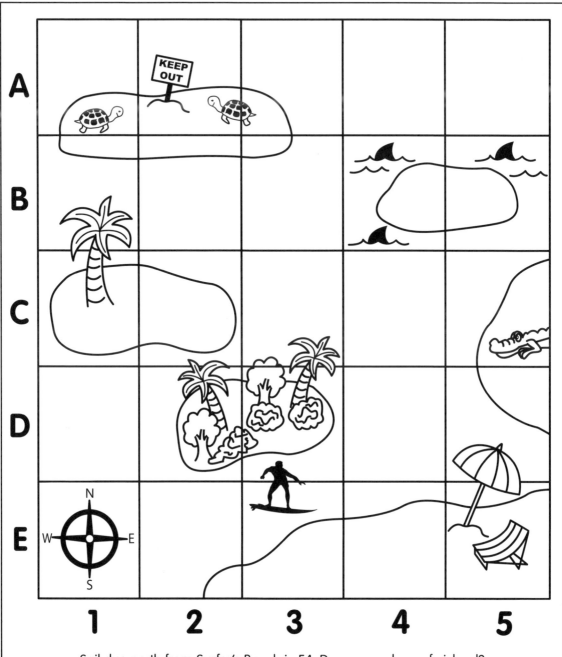

Sail due north from Surfer's Beach in E4. Do you reach a safe island?

Sail northwest for one square. Can you stay on this island?

Sail directly south for two squares. Is this island any good?

Which squares would you visit to find a better island?

Can you find 15 seaside words hidden in the grid? All of them begin with S.

```
S  E  L  T  S  A  C  D  N  A  S
S  U  S  A  N  D  A  L  S  S  T
H  E  E  S  U  S  U  U  W  U  A
O  S  A  S  S  E  N  S  I  N  R
R  W  G  W  A  B  S  A  M  B  F
E  I  U  S  E  N  E  N  S  L  I
L  M  L  D  U  E  A  D  U  O  S
L  M  L  S  A  N  D  W  I  C  H
E  E  S  S  U  N  H  A  T  K  S
H  R  S  A  N  S  P  A  D  E  E
S  S  D  R  A  O  B  F  R  U  S
```

SURFBOARD   SWIMSUIT

SEAWEED   SANDWICH

SUNHAT   SANDALS

SEAGULL   STARFISH

SHORE   SANDCASTLE

SPADE   SWIMMER

SHELL   SUNBLOCK

SUNBED

This game is great for a sunny day at the beach or in the garden.

WET AND WILD

The rules to this game are simple, but it's fantastic fun. All you need are some water bomb balloons. Fill them quite full and ask an adult to tie the ends.

Stand in a circle and throw the water bomb from player to player. Make sure you catch the bomb or you will get splashed. You also have to be careful how you catch it. If you squeeze it too hard it will burst all over you!

If it's too easy, shout out a name as you throw the bomb – but don't always shout the name of the person you are throwing to! Make the game more fun (and splashy) by throwing the water bombs high in the air, or throw more than one water bomb around the circle.

SPLASH!

Use the picture clues to fill in the answers in the crossword grid.

Grid answers (as filled in):

1. plane
3. sword
6. tr...
7. nest
8. vase
9. spade
10. f...
11. vitch
12. n...
13. t...
14. dea...
15. euro
16. hippo
17. cloud

ACROSS

1.
3.
7.
8.
9.
11.
14.
15.
16.
17.

DOWN

1.
2.
4.
5.
6.
10.
11.
12.
13.

Look for numbers in the 3x table to get through the water park to the wave pool.

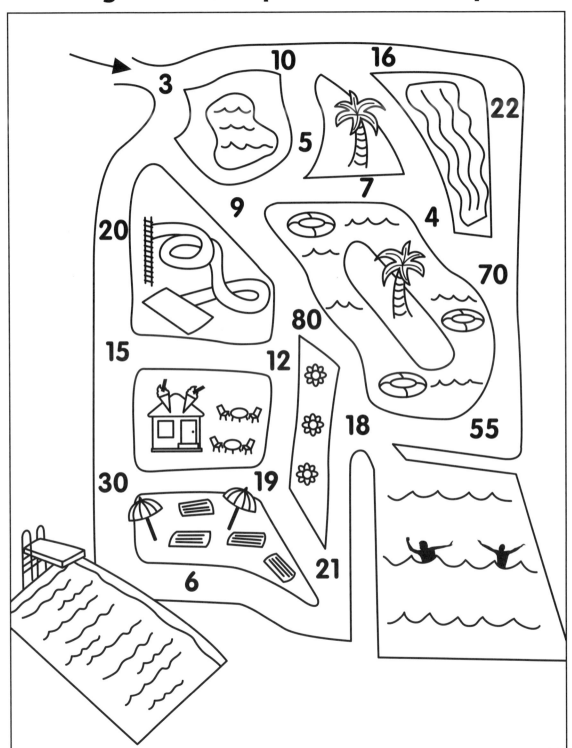

Only two of these snakes have matching patterns. Can you see which two?

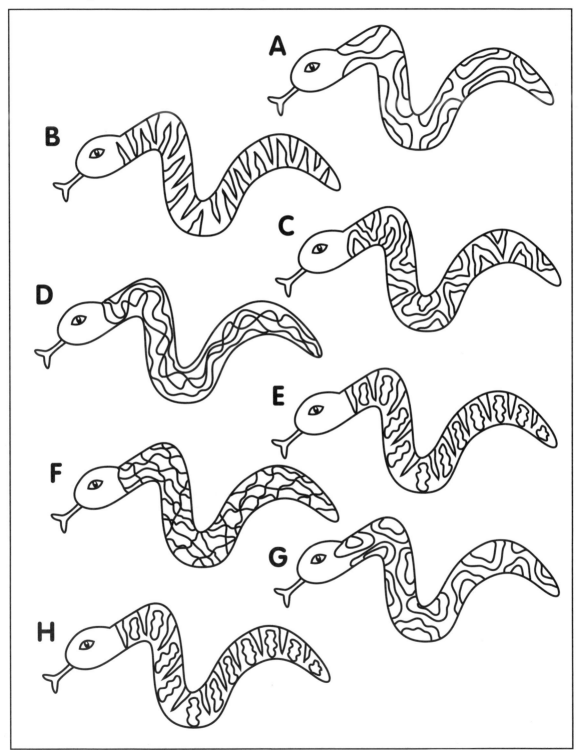

Here's a game to test your brainpower when you're stuck in a vehicle for ages.

RHYME TIME

One player goes first and says a word out loud. It can be any simple word, like 'house' or 'train'.

Every other player takes a turn to say a word that rhymes. Score a point if you think of a proper rhyme that no one has said before. Lose a point if you shout out when it isn't your turn, or if you say a nonsense word or repeat someone else's word.

When all the rhyming words have been said, let someone else choose a word.

See who can be the first player to score 25 points.

FRIES

What's growing in the garden?

BIG FOOT

Divide the players into two teams. You can play with just two people if that's all you have. Each team needs a pair of really BIG shoes or swimming flippers.

> **Make a starting line and a finish line. Draw them in the sand or with chalk or pebbles. Put the Big Foot shoes on the starting line in front of each team or player.**

Start when someone says "Go!" Put on the Big Foot shoes and race towards the finish line. Turn around and run back again. Be careful that you don't fall and hurt yourself. If you lose a shoe you have to stop and put it back on before you can carry on racing.

> **If you're playing in teams, take it in turns to wear the Big Foot shoes and race to the finish line and back again. The winner is, of course, the team that finishes first.**

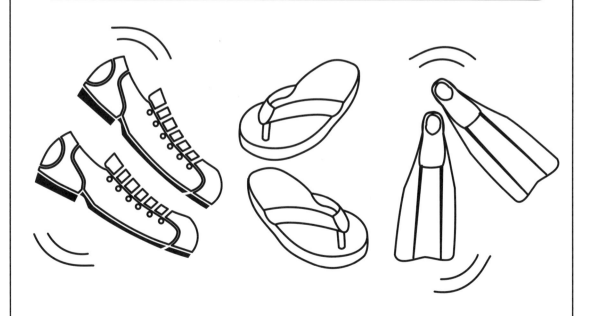

Solve the sudoku puzzles so that every row, column and mini-grid has the six symbols.

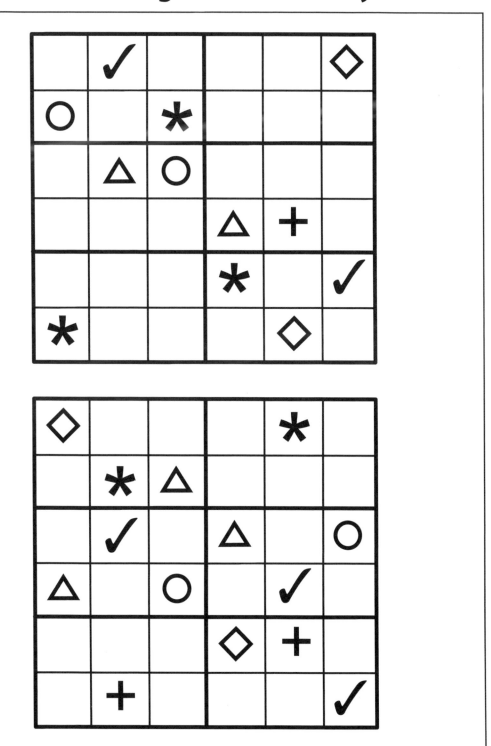

Use the grid references to answer the questions about this farm.

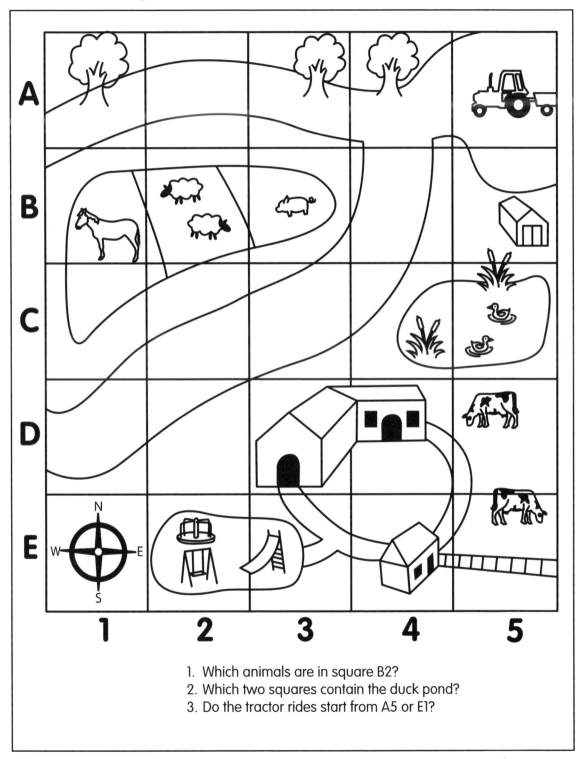

1. Which animals are in square B2?
2. Which two squares contain the duck pond?
3. Do the tractor rides start from A5 or E1?

47

Don't get bored on a long journey
— get brainier!

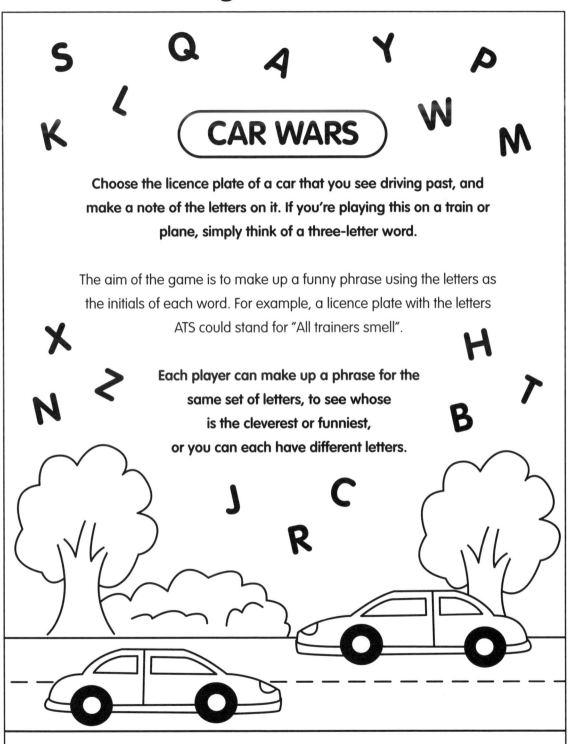

CAR WARS

Choose the licence plate of a car that you see driving past, and make a note of the letters on it. If you're playing this on a train or plane, simply think of a three-letter word.

The aim of the game is to make up a funny phrase using the letters as the initials of each word. For example, a licence plate with the letters ATS could stand for "All trainers smell".

Each player can make up a phrase for the same set of letters, to see whose is the cleverest or funniest, or you can each have different letters.

Can you identify the ten vehicles and find their names in the grid?

```
P F N X H F A X M B
O L W C S G M I O H
E S A D E M V A T P
P O B N R T T Q O G
C Q I Y E R C A R B
D L C B A U C N B O
J V Y H T C R U I L
C I C K Y K H J K T
H E L I C O P T E R
Z K E M O P E D A U
```

Gather together as many players as you can to make this outdoor game even more fun.

WHAT TIME IS IT?

Choose one player to be "It". In this game he is known as Mr Wolf. He stands about 10 metres from the other players, with his back turned.

The players all shout, "**What time is it, Mr Wolf?**" He answers with any time he likes, for example, "**Eight o'clock!**" The players must take eight steps towards him. If he turns around to look at them, they must instantly freeze until he turns away again.

Carry on asking the time until Mr Wolf answers,

"Dinner time!"

Or someone gets close enough to tap him on the shoulder.

Then Mr Wolf has to chase everyone back to the start line. If he catches someone, it is their turn to be Mr Wolf.

Colour in this crazy clown!

Solve the clues to fill in the crossword grid.

1.		2.		3.		4.
		5.		6.			
	7.					8.	
|9.|					
10.		11.		12.		13.	
14.|						

ACROSS

1. Black and white mammal from North and South America
5. A short word for a friend
9. The one after fourth
11. Insect swallowed by the old lady in the rhyme
14. North African country popular for holidays

DOWN

1. Bone in your chest
2. Drink coffee from this
3. A night bird
4. A short sleep
6. Bad, appalling, horrendous
7. Opposite of on
8. Someone who goes quiet with strangers is this
10. Wear it on your head
11. A sports supporter
12. Nodding your head shows you mean this
13. The noise made by a sheep

Use the compass at the top of the map to help answer the questions.

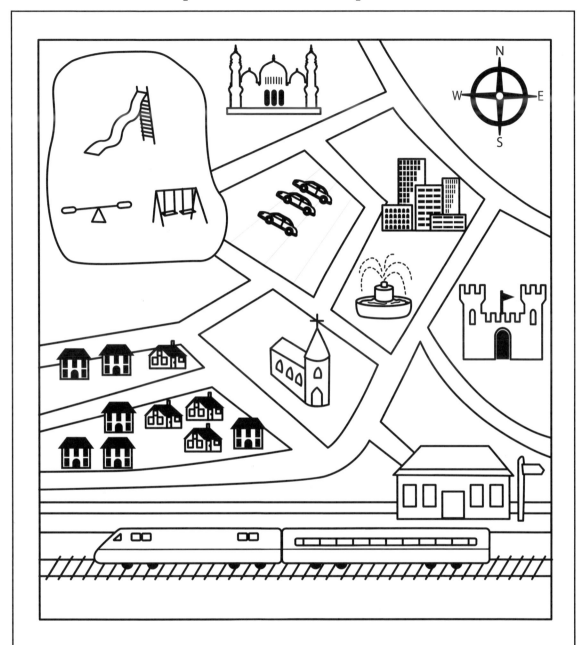

1. Is the mosque in the north or south of the town?

2. Which side of the town is the castle?

3. Do you walk north or south from the fountain to get to the station?

You need pens and paper to play this simple travelling game.

ALPHABATTY

Write the letters of the alphabet down the side of your paper. The aim of the game is to spot something that begins with each letter, for example an army truck, a bottle bank, a car, a dog…you get the idea. Write down each item as you spot it.

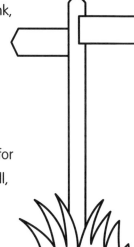

Set a time limit and when the time is up, stop writing. Compare your list to the other players' lists. Score a point for every item that is on another list as well, and two points for an item that no one else has spotted.

If you want to make this game much harder, add a new rule: you cannot spot an item beginning with 'b' until you have found one beginning with 'a', and so on.

Study the parrots carefully and then answer the question.

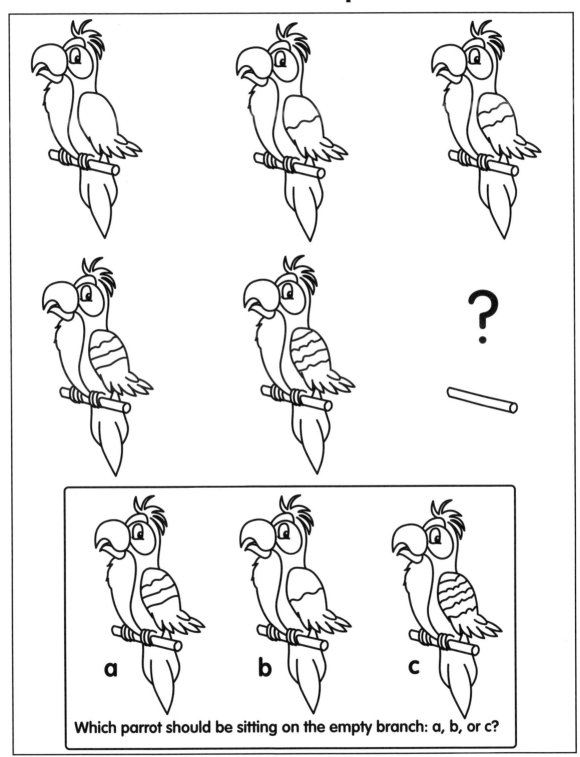

Which parrot should be sitting on the empty branch: a, b, or c?

Fill in the missing letters to spell the names of 6 islands around the world.

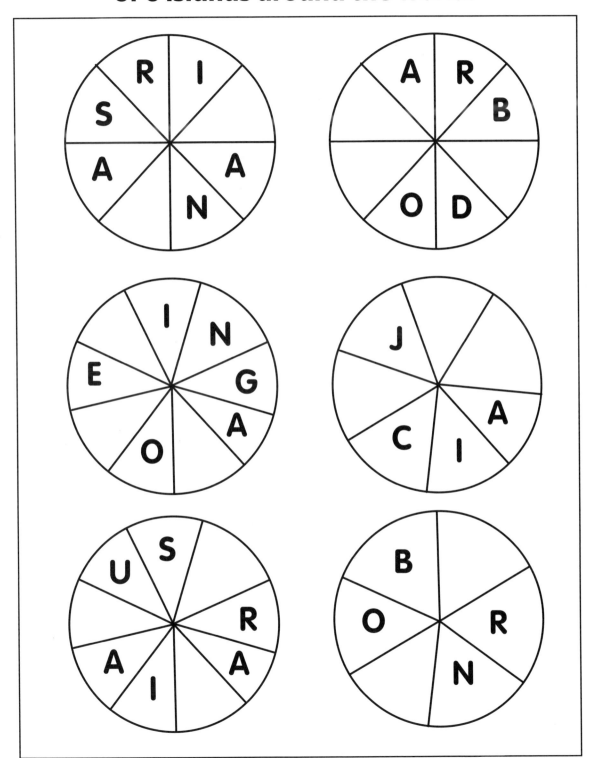

This outdoor game is the most fun with lots of players.

QUEENIO

Choose one player to be Queenio. She stands with her back to the other players, holding a ball. She throws the ball behind her for any of the other players to catch.

The players all line up with their hands behind their back. The player with the ball has to keep it hidden in his hands, and the others have to act as though they might be holding the ball. Then they all chant together,
"Queenio, queenio, who's got the ball-i-o?!"

Queenio turns round and must try to figure out who is hiding the ball. She can shout "Switch!" and run through the line of players to catch them out – but they are allowed to change direction to face her again. They can also pass the ball behind their backs, as long as they don't get spotted.

When Queenio guesses who has the ball, the person who was hiding it becomes Queenio.

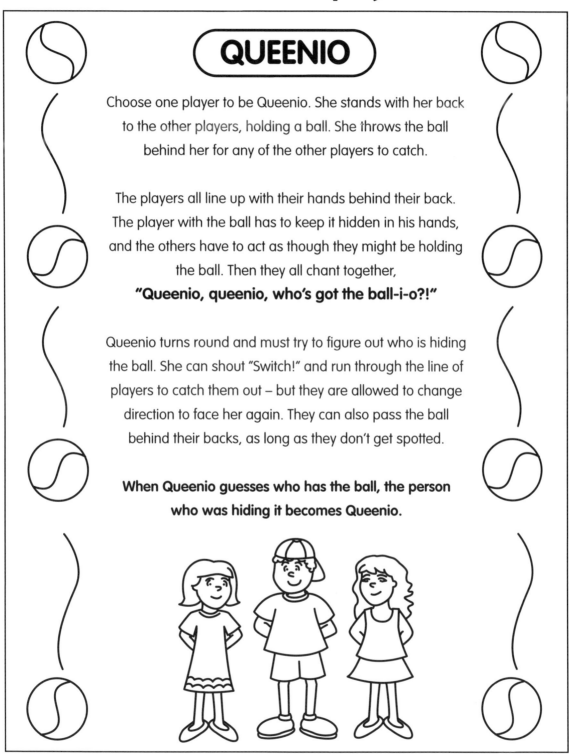

Which picture of the Leaning Tower of Pisa is the odd one out?

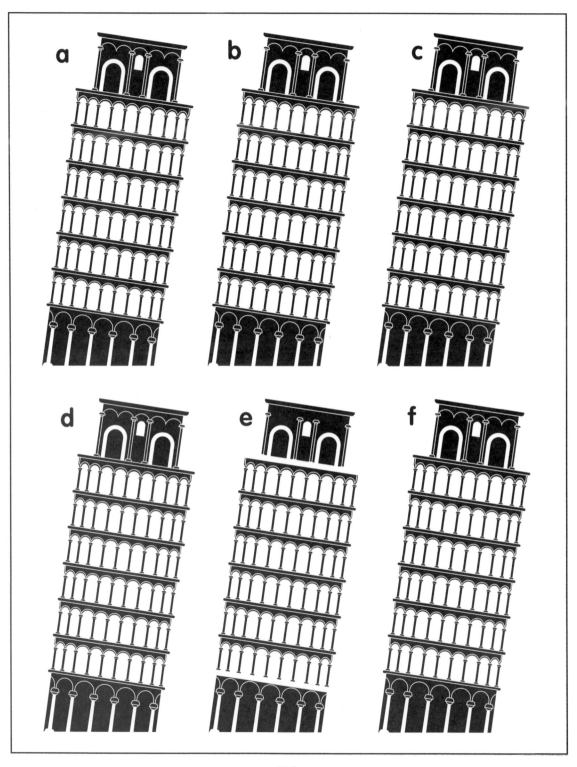

Follow the arrows to guide the frog prince across the pond, without jumping on any other frogs.

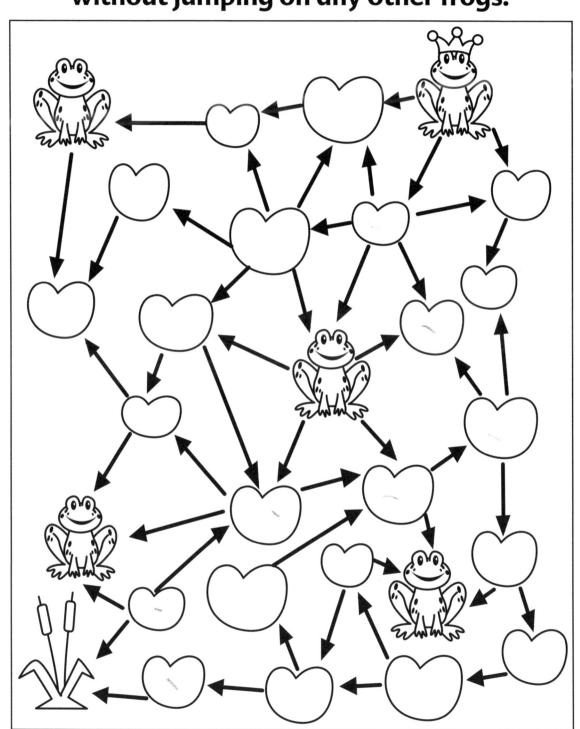

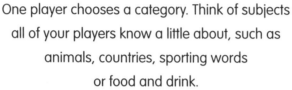

A TO Z

One player chooses a category. Think of subjects all of your players know a little about, such as animals, countries, sporting words or food and drink.

Take it in turns to name something from that category, each beginning with A. Let's imagine your topic is food and drink: you could say apple, aubergine, apple juice, asparagus and anchovies. Yum!

When every player has said something, without repeating a word that has already been chosen, move on to B. Let the next player in the playing order go first (otherwise the same person always speaks last and the game is much harder for them).

It's fun to play this game in its simplest form, but if you want to, you can play for points. Anyone who repeats a word or can't think of an item scores a point. If you score five points you're out of the game.

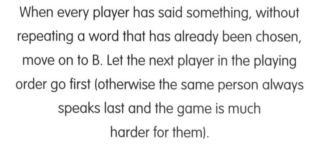

Solve the sudoku puzzle so that every row, column and mini-grid has the letters A to F.

E	B	F			
				E	
		E		C	
	A		B		
	F				
			D	F	C

C		F			
D	B		C		
				B	
	E				
		C		E	F
			B		D

Finish the picture of the alien.

How many times can you count the word SUN and RAIN in the grids?

Use the grid references to answer questions about the map of the museum.

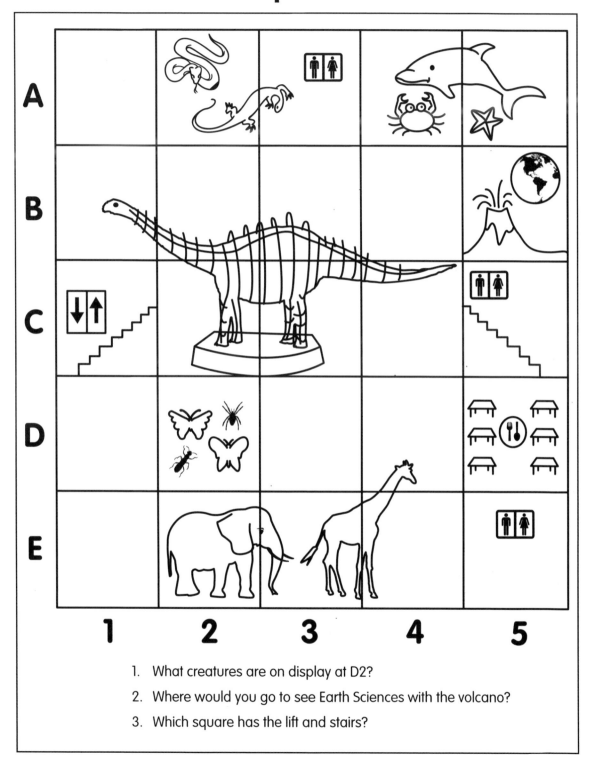

1. What creatures are on display at D2?

2. Where would you go to see Earth Sciences with the volcano?

3. Which square has the lift and stairs?

Use the price labels to answer the questions in the 'Around the World' souvenir shop.

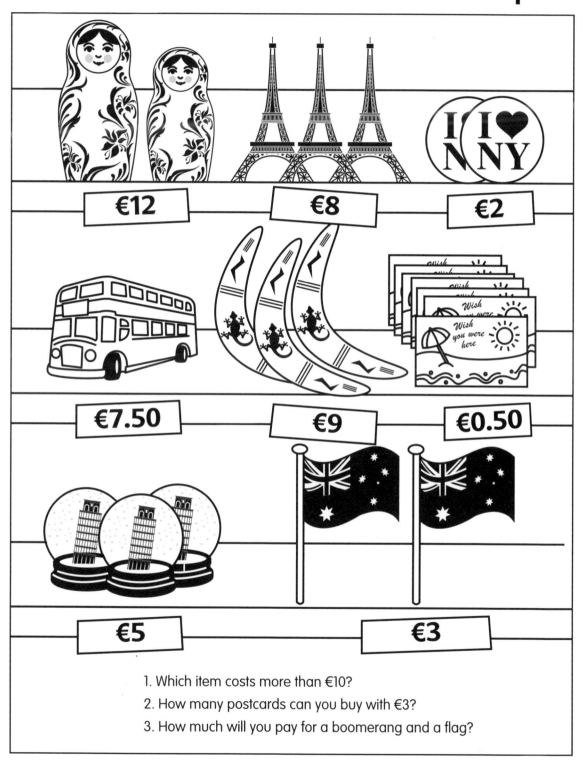

€12

€8

€2

€7.50

€9

€0.50

€5

€3

1. Which item costs more than €10?

2. How many postcards can you buy with €3?

3. How much will you pay for a boomerang and a flag?

Can you spot 6 differences between these two pictures?

Find a wide open space to run around with your friends.

STUCK IN THE MUD

This game is best with lots of players.
One person is **It** and has to try to catch the others.
(If there are more than ten players,
choose two people to be **It**.)

Any player who is caught has to stand still with their
legs spread apart. They cannot move until another
free player crawls between their legs to
release them. Of course, it's easier for **It** to catch
a player if she is crawling through someone's
legs, so watch out!

Take turns to be **It** so that
nobody gets bored of
always having to chase
the others.

Look carefully at the scene, then work out which overhead picture matches it exactly.

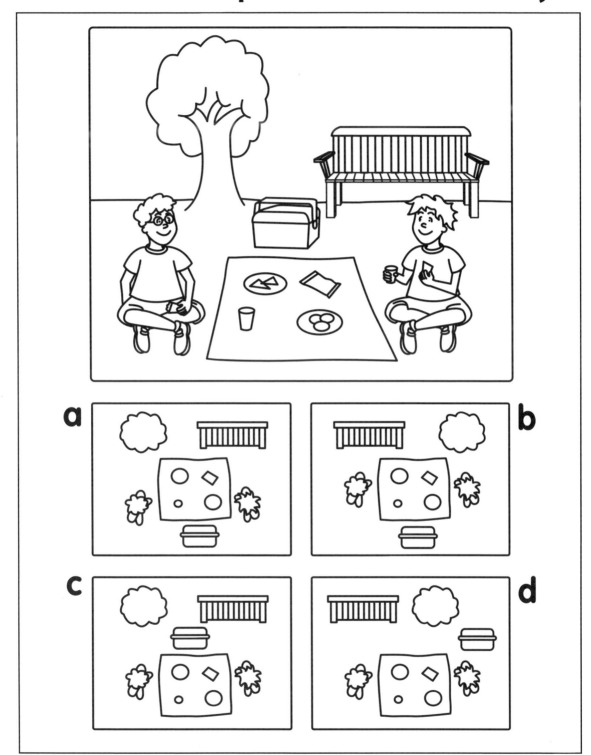

AROUND THE WORLD

eXSten

your way through the tyre maze.

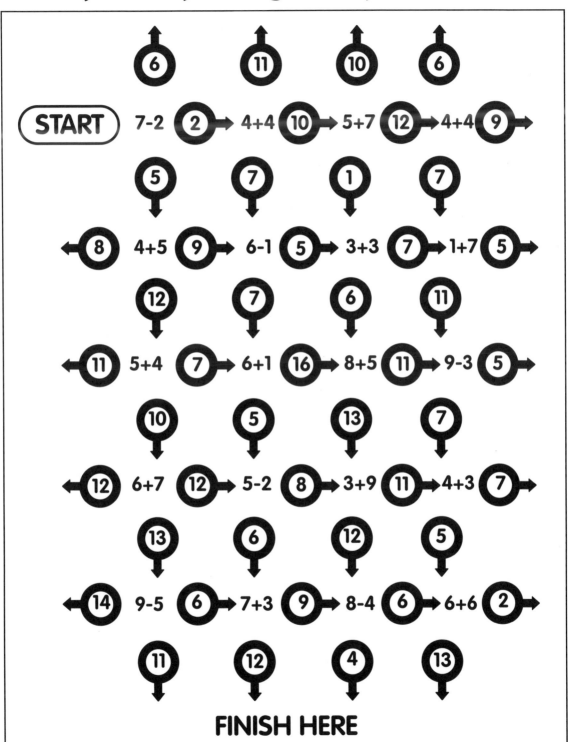

skateboard belongs to Joe.

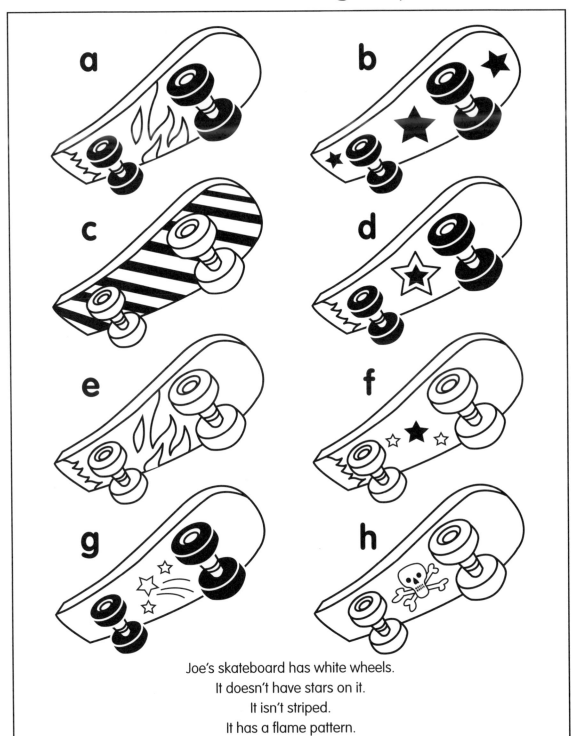

Joe's skateboard has white wheels.
It doesn't have stars on it.
It isn't striped.
It has a flame pattern.

72

WALK

_T_ _A_ _L_ _K_ Speak

_T_ _A_ _L_ _E_ Fairy Story

_T_ _I_ _L_ _E_ Wall covering

_T_ _I_ _D_ _E_ Ocean movement

RIDE

BOAT

_C_ _O_ _A_ _t_ Jacket

_—_ _—_ _—_ _—_ Talk

_—_ _—_ _—_ _—_ Man

_—_ _—_ _—_ _—_ Potato snack

SHIP

1. Honolulu

2. Basket b

3.

4	3	6	5	1	**2**
2	**1**	5	**3**	6	**4**
1	4	3	2	**5**	6
6	5	2	1	4	**3**
3	6	1	**4**	2	5
5	2	4	6	3	1

6	**3**	2	4	5	**1**
1	5	4	**2**	3	6
2	6	5	3	1	4
4	1	3	**5**	**6**	**2**
5	**2**	6	**1**	4	3
3	**4**	1	6	2	5

5.

6. $4 + 3 - 5 = 2$

   $5 \times 5 = 25$

   $12 \div 2 = 6$

   $22 - 7 + 15 = 30$

7.

9. The treasure is in the
   plants in D4.

10.

¹S	T	²A	T	³I	O	⁴N
E	■	N	■	C	■	E
A	■	⁵T	⁶I	E	■	T
■	⁷A	■	T	■	⁸R	■
■	⁹C	Y	C	L	E	■
■	E	■	H	■	D	■
¹⁰C	■	¹¹B	Y	¹²E	■	¹³F
A	■	O	■	E	■	L
¹⁴R	O	Y	A	L	T	Y

74

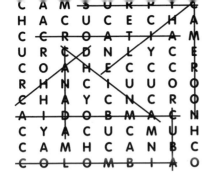

12.

```
  C A M S U R P Y C
H A C U C E C H A
C C R O A T I A M
U R C D N L Y C E
C O A H E C C C R
R H N C I U U O O
C H A Y C N C R O
A I D O B M A C N
C Y A C U C M U H
C A M H C A N B C
C O L O M B I A O
```

13.

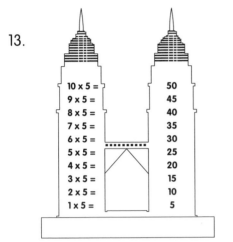

10 x 5 =	50
9 x 5 =	45
8 x 5 =	40
7 x 5 =	35
6 x 5 =	30
5 x 5 =	25
4 x 5 =	20
3 x 5 =	15
2 x 5 =	10
1 x 5 =	5

15.

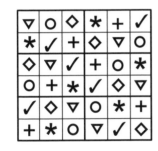

17. Silhouette e

18. They spend Krone in Denmark.
South African currency
is the Rand.
1. Pound   2. Dollar
3. Rupee   4. Euro

19.

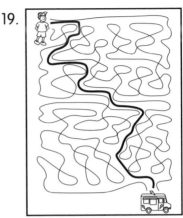

20. Australia = Canberra
Austria = Vienna
Belgium = Brussels
Bulgaria = Sofia
Canada = Ottawa
China = Beijing
Czech Republic = Prague
Denmark = Copenhagen
Ecuador = Quito
Egypt = Cairo
France = Paris
Germany = Berlin
Ghana = Accra
Hungary = Budapest
Italy = Rome
Japan = Tokyo
New Zealand = Wellington

Norway = Oslo

Peru = Lima

Russia = Moscow

Spain = Madrid

Switzerland = Bern

United Kingdom = London

USA = Washington DC

Venezuela = Caracas

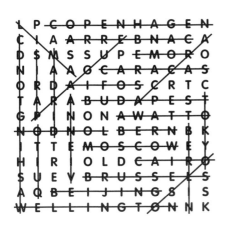

Something you pass in the airport is the PASSPORT CONTROL DESK

23. 1. West
    2. Southwest
    3. North

24. 9 flags

25.

F	**A**	**B**	**C**	D	E
E	C	D	A	**F**	B
D	B	**F**	E	A	**C**
C	E	A	**F**	B	D
B	**F**	E	D	C	A
A	D	**C**	**B**	**E**	F

A	F	**C**	D	E	B
B	**E**	D	A	**F**	C
D	A	B	E	C	**F**
E	C	F	B	D	A
F	**D**	A	C	**B**	**E**
C	B	E	**F**	A	**D**

27.

30.

76

31.

```
S A N I A M W A L B J
B W G S S O T B K S A
R S I R R B R S K A P
S O U T H A F R I C A
P A E A Z E B A N C N
C C S I F E G L D S M
H H L A M O R O C C O
I   S O U F R L G A R
L N N A T S I K A P J
S A N E C E E R G N A
W A L E S I B R A Z D
```

BRAZIL
CHINA
GREECE
ISRAEL
JAPAN
MOROCCO
PAKISTAN
SOUTH AFRICA
SWITZERLAND
WALES

35.

2	4	**1**	3	5	6
5	6	**3**	2	**4**	1
6	3	5	4	1	**2**
4	1	2	5	**6**	3
3	**5**	6	1	2	4
1	2	4	6	3	**5**

1	**6**	3	**4**	**5**	2
2	5	4	**1**	3	6
3	**1**	**5**	6	2	4
4	2	6	3	1	5
6	3	2	5	4	1
5	**4**	1	2	6	**3**

32.

33. EIFFEL TOWER

TAJ MAHAL

LONDON EYE

OPERA HOUSE

37. No, it has too many sharks.

No, it is for turtles laying eggs.

No, it is too overgrown.

The best island is in C1 and C2.

38.

```
S E L T S A C D N A S
S U S A N D A L S S T
H E E S U S U U W U A
O S A S S E N S N R
R W G W A B S A M B F
E I U S E N E N S L I
L M L D U E A D U O S
L M L S A N D W I C H
E E S S U N H A T K S
H R S A N S P A D E E
S S D R A O B F R U S
```

40.

¹P	L	A	²N	E		³S	⁴W	O	R	⁵D
E			U		⁶T		A			E
⁷N	E	S	T		R		⁸V	A	S	E
S			⁹S	P	A	D	E			R
					C					
¹⁰F			¹¹W	I	T	C	¹²H			¹³T
¹⁴I	D	E	A		O		¹⁵E	U	R	O
S			S		R		E			A
¹⁶H	I	P	P	O		¹⁷C	L	O	U	D

41.

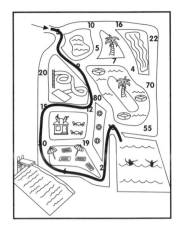

42. E and H

46.

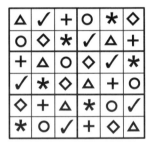

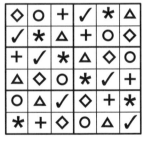

47. 1. Sheep
2. C4 and C5
3. A5

49.

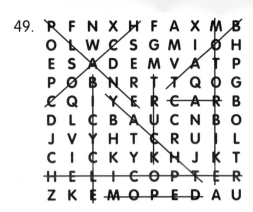

BICYCLE   MOPED
CAR   HELICOPTER
COACH   PLANE
TRUCK   BOAT
MOTORBIKE   YACHT

52.

53. 1. North
2. East
3. South

55. c

56. SRI LANKA
    BARBADOS
    SINGAPORE
    JAMAICA
    AUSTRALIA
    BORNEO

58. e

59.
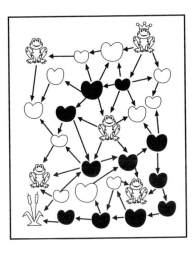

61.

E	B	F	C	A	D
D	C	A	F	E	B
B	D	E	A	C	F
F	A	C	B	D	E
C	F	D	E	B	A
A	E	B	D	F	C

C	A	F	E	D	B
D	B	E	C	F	A
A	C	D	F	B	E
F	E	B	D	A	C
B	D	C	A	E	F
E	F	A	B	C	D

63.
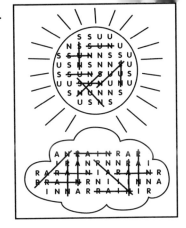

SUN appears 9 times
RAIN appears 11 times

64. 1. Insects
    2. B5
    3. C1

65. 1. Russian dolls
    2. 6 postcards
    3. €12

66.

68. c

69. Here are just a few:

NEW

WON

DRAW

OLD

DOWN

REAL

THROW

RETURN

HOWLER

but there are lots!

73. WALK

TALK

TALE

TILE

TIDE

RIDE

BOAT

COAT

CHAT

CHAP

CHIP

SHIP

71.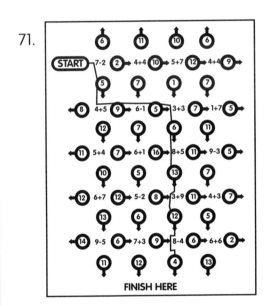

72. e